ART ATTACK ™

Hi! Welcome to Art Attack! In this book I am going to let you in on some great Art Attack secrets and show you some brilliant ideas for your own Art Attacks. Come on in, and let's make art!

Neil Buchanan

WAX CRAYON

My Family

It's always fun to personalize things and that's what this book is about. So, if I tell you lots of things about me, will you fill in the details about you?

One way of explaining about yourself is to draw a family tree. You can do it in words or, better still, use photographs or drawings of your family. And that can mean your brothers and sisters, your mum and dad and your grandparents. If you like, you could even include aunts, uncles and cousins.

On a family tree, the side-to-side lines mean that people are brother and sister. Up-and-down lines mean that people are parents and children. Dotted side-to-side lines mean that people have married.

NOW TRY IT YOURSELF.

Now, here's a sample family tree.

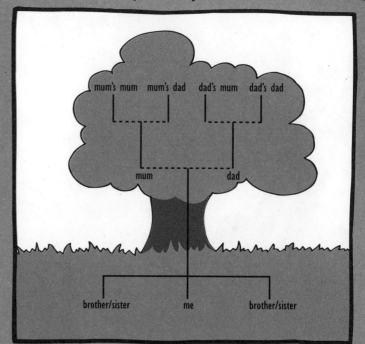

mum's mum   mum's dad   dad's mum   dad's dad

mum   dad

brother/sister   me   brother/sister

Add your family's dates of birth to the tree.

2

My Fact File

Now it's time to personalize this Art Attack book and tell me about yourself.

My name is

I live at

I go to school at

My age is

My brothers and sisters are called

My height is

The colour of my eyes is

The colour of my hair is

My favourite actor is

My favourite pop star is

My favourite clothes are

Place your picture here.

All About Neil

My favourite colours are
Blue for clothes
Red for Liverpool football team
Silver for cars

My favourite artist is
Walt Disney

My hobbies are
Birdwatching and flying

My favourite foods are
Chocolate, curry and chips

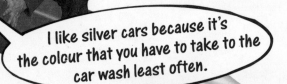

I like silver cars because it's the colour that you have to take to the car wash least often.

My bad habits are
Fiddling with anything to turn it into a picture
Doodling when people are talking or I am talking on the 'phone

I have done pictures with chocolate and chips ... but I haven't tried curry yet!

I get my best ideas
In the shower and on holiday

My favourite TV programme is
Art Attack!

My least favourite thing about Art Attack
The Head's silly jokes (not really!)

All About Me

My favourite colours are

My favourite artist is

My favourite food is

My hobbies are

My favourite TV programme is

My best ideas are

My bad habits are

Amazing Autographs

Have you ever thought about being a pop star or movie star? Fame, fortune and all those autographs you'd have to sign?

Well, even if you're not a star yet, you might as well start practising your autograph now. It should be something stylish to look at, but quick to do ... because, who knows, you may need to write it hundreds of times a day!

1

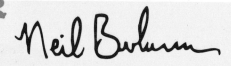

Here's my name. It's not very clear, not very stylish and ... not very special.

2

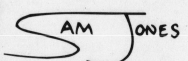

First, capital letters make it clearer. Now, let's add some personality to it. I'll make the initials bigger and join them up.

3

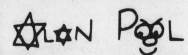

Or I can start with my initials, and then fill in the rest of my name around them. Here's the final version of my autograph.

Here are a few more ideas to try. I'm using my friends' names.

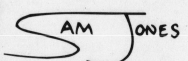

Make your initials big and join them up.

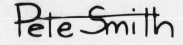

Join up some of the other letters like these Ts.

Join the initials vertically on top of each other.

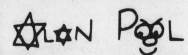

Personalize your letters by adding things in, like stars or faces.

Use a first name and wrap some of the letters in the name around the others.

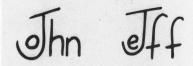

Try missing out a letter and putting it somewhere else.

You could just use your initials like this, and put one initial facing the wrong way, or put one inside the other.

And if you have two initials the same, you can have great fun.

6

CRAYON

NOW, YOU CAN PRACTISE ALL THESE IDEAS.

And please can I have your autograph?

TO NEIL,
BEST WISHES,
FROM

You probably want mine too, Neil, so here it is.

Head

Face Map

Do you have trouble drawing faces? Do they never look quite right?

Well, here's an easy tip to make sure you get all the bits in the right places. Draw a face map!

1

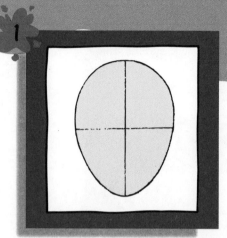

Draw an egg shape that is slightly taller than wide. Draw a line to divide it in half from top to bottom, and another that divides it in half from side to side.

2

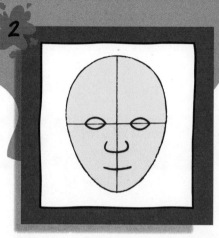

Draw the eyes on the side-to-side line and the nose and the mouth on the top-to-bottom line. There it is – a face map with all the bits in the right places.

3

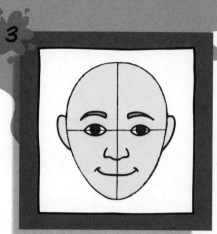

Now put in the detail – eyes and eyebrows, shape the nose, widen the mouth into a smile, put the ears roughly level with the eyes.

Use a light pencil for your face map so that you can rub out the guidelines later.

Use the face map to make sure the eyes are not too far up the head.

4

Now we can shape the cheeks and chin, add a neck and put on hair at the side and top. Rub out your face map lines.

Here are some eggs for you to practise on. Try all kinds of different people.

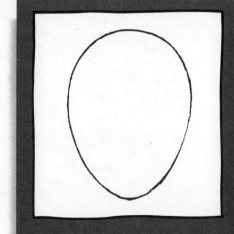
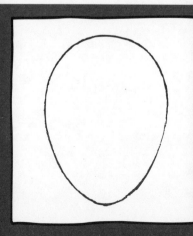
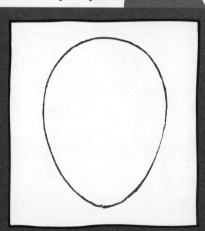

8

So that works easily if you are looking face-on. But how do you draw a face looking sideways, or up or down? Here's how.

1

If looking sideways, move the nose line to the side.

2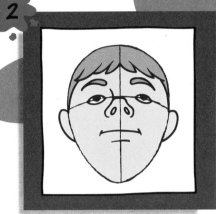

If looking up, move the eyeline up a bit. Now you can see more chin.

3

If looking down, move the eyeline down a bit. Now you can see more hair.

NOW, TRY IT YOURSELF.

So now you really *can* make someone an egghead. Ha Ha!

Fun with Faces

SYMMETRICAL FACES

When is half a picture a whole picture? Like this, when you make a face using only half a photograph.

Cut a face from a magazine and cut it in half. Stick one half down on a piece of paper and draw in the other half. Now colour in the drawn side in different ways.

This one's in pencil.   This one's in paint.   This one's in coloured paper.

Try lots of materials for colouring. The effect is always different.

HERE'S A FEW FOR YOU TO TRY.

10

NEW HAIRCUT KIT

Do you ever wonder what you would look like with another hairstyle? Well, try this before you have a disaster at the hairdresser's.

Find a photograph of yourself, as face-on as possible.

Cover it with tracing paper and trace around your face, leaving out your hair.

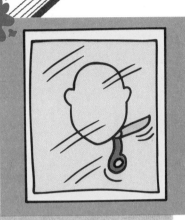

Cut out the face area.

Use the tracing as a template and draw around your head shape. Do lots of them.

Now draw a different hairstyle on each face shape. Cut out the faces. Put your photo behind each style to see what you look like.

Big Art Attacks

My **FAVOURITE** Big Art Attack was a picture of a jumbo jet made out of suitcases and other bits of holiday luggage.

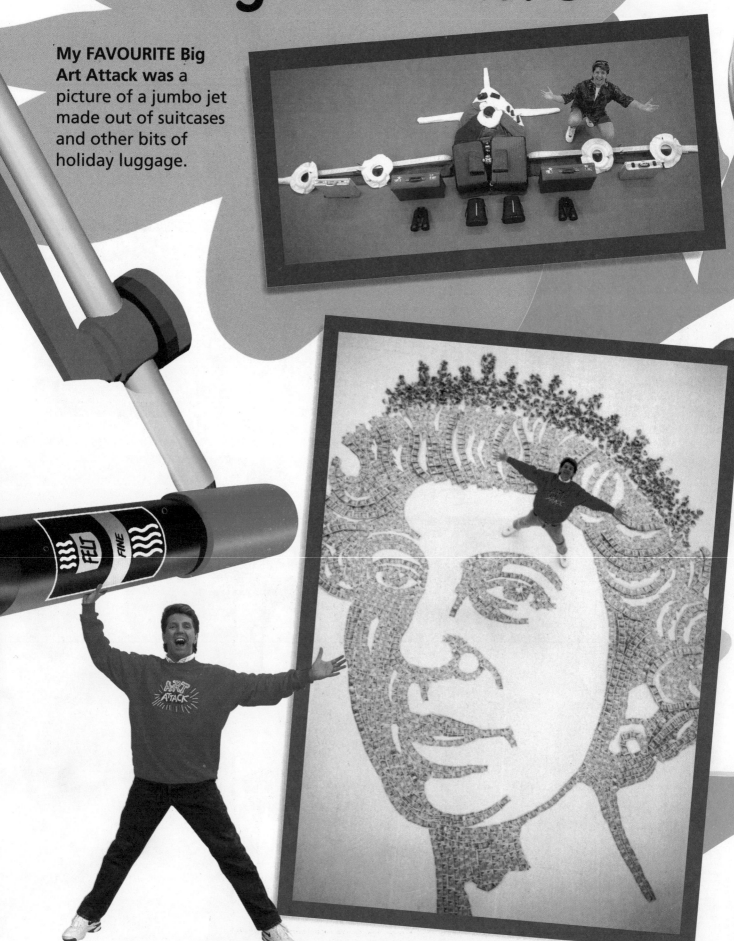

But the MOST EXPENSIVE was ... a portrait of Her Majesty, Queen Elizabeth II using a quarter of a million pounds. And I had to give the money back at the end!

12

The HOTTEST ... a picture of Father Christmas on a beach in Barbados. I had to stay under an umbrella all day and only come out for two minutes at a time to do the picture.

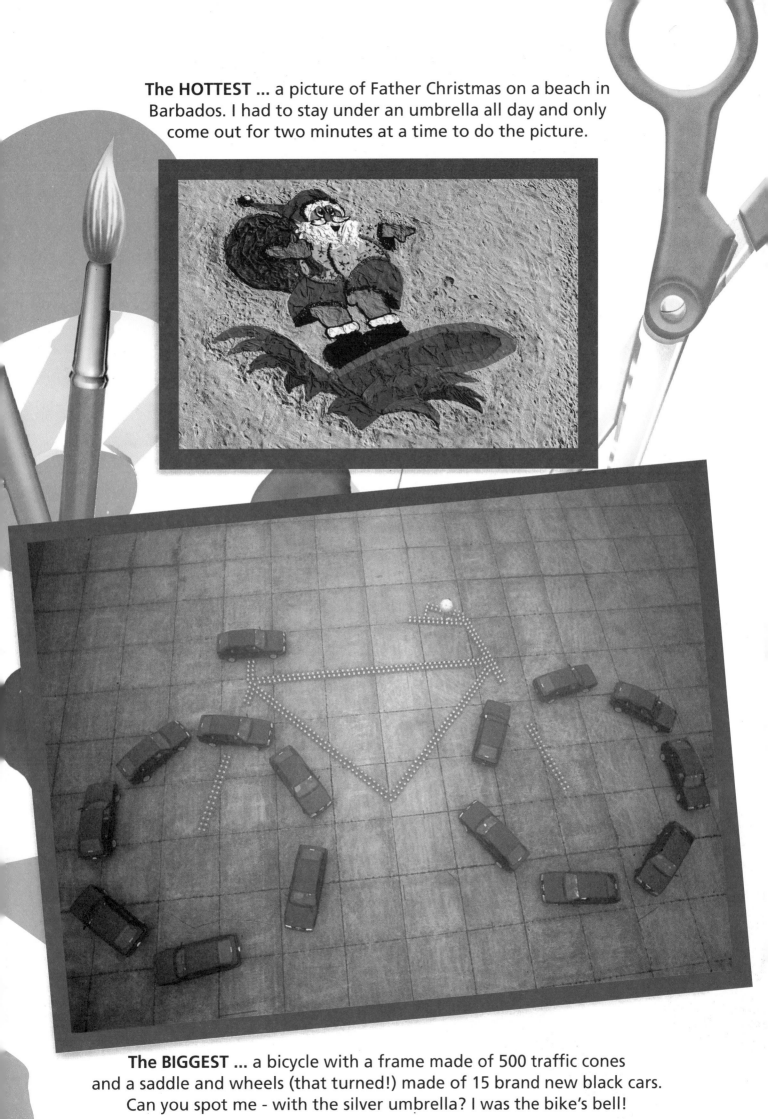

The BIGGEST ... a bicycle with a frame made of 500 traffic cones and a saddle and wheels (that turned!) made of 15 brand new black cars. Can you spot me - with the silver umbrella? I was the bike's bell!

Alphabet Attack

I love playing with letters and words. And, as you know, they come in all shapes and sizes like this ...

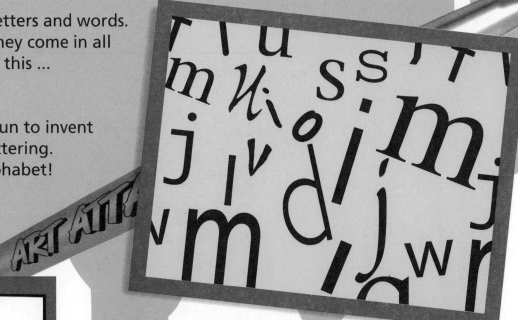

But it's much more fun to invent your own style of lettering. Design your own alphabet!

1

Start by inventing a style for your letters. This one's not going to have any curves in it! Here's an A which is pointy and sharp.

Keep a neat copy of your alphabet and refer to it when you write something.

2

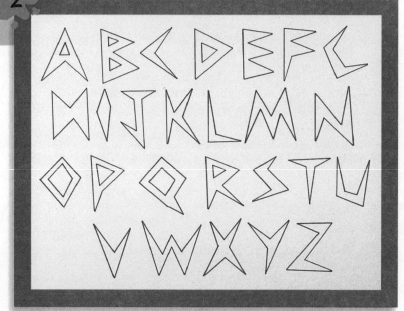

Now I can add the rest of the letters. The ones which have straight lines are easy, but curvy letters, like S and R, need thinking about.

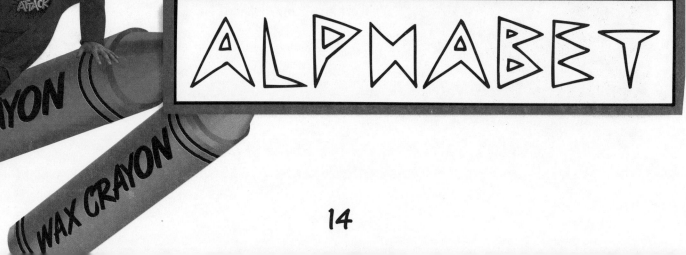

14

Arty Words

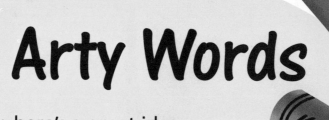

Now, here's a great idea. Making words look like their meaning.

Here's one to begin with. I've drawn chunky letters for wood.

Now I've added the detail. I've thickened it up with a shadow, drawn in some grain lines and added some knots. I've even drawn in some nails, where the wood is nailed together!

Here are some more.

NOW TRY IT YOURSELF.

sheep

water

spaghetti

jeans

16

Illuminated Letters

Here's more fun with words. Some words can just look dull,

so here's a way of turning them into

that no one can miss. And they certainly light up the page!

Take a sheet of patterned paper – wallpaper, wrapping paper or cut something out of a magazine. Draw your letter on it and cut it out.

Take some more patterned paper and cut it into a square, larger than your letter. Glue the letter on to it to give it a contrasting background.

Outline the letter and background square with a gold pen.

Make sure your letter and base square go together. Try purple on pink!

There are lots of other things you can do to jazz up these letters.

You could put your letter on a plain piece of paper and doodle around the edges with a coloured pen.

Put on some frills. Put your square on its background and draw half way round a 2p coin to make a frilly border.

Pop Art

I like turning things around me into small Art Attacks. All kinds of everyday objects give me ideas. Packaging is one of my favourites – it is covered in graphic designs, logos and emblems. So how about a bit of pop-swap art?

Copy the design into the first section and then copy it, or trace it into all the other sections.

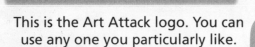

This is the Art Attack logo. You can use any one you particularly like.

Colour in the first section like the original.

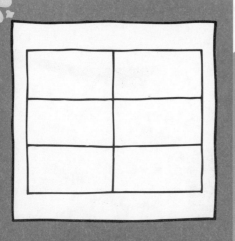

Take a large piece of white paper and divide it into sections – as many as you like, as long as they are big enough for the logo.

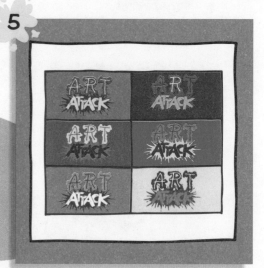

Then swap the colours around, like this. Try different colours in different sections.

18

NOW INVENT YOUR OWN LOGO.

Jazzy Magazine Borders

Most pictures look better with a frame or border. And so do notebooks, pencil tins and ... well, anything else that you can think of. And the source of your frames is easy. Use up all those old magazines that you have lying around!

Cut lots of small pictures out of magazines. Anything will do, but it is a good idea to choose themes, such as pop stars, animals or food.

You can do the border all the way round or just at the corners.

Now choose what you want to decorate, and start to piece together the pictures in a border around the edges.

Glue the pictures in place with a mixture of half PVA glue and half water. Paint the mixture all over and leave to dry.

This idea is so simple that you can use it on old picture frames and even mirrors. See how this old make-up mirror looks really good with a border.

Be VERY careful when handling glass.

Draw round the mirror on a piece of card.

Put the mirror to one side and put your magazine bits around the edges. Glue them on to the card and leave to dry.

Cut out your frame and stick your mirror on to it.

Here are two frames to practise on. Stick your magazine items on the frame and draw in a picture to match the theme.

Close Encounters

Do you think there is life on other planets? Do aliens really exist? What do they look like? Are they scary monsters? See how you can turn yourself into an alien.

Draw a simple picture of yourself in pencil, or trace a photograph.

Take each feature and do something horrible with it. Here are huge eyes with crazy pupils and four eyelids.

Wrinkle up the nose and widen the nostrils.

Make two top lips and two bottom lips. Make them thin and add some fangs and pointy teeth.

Point up the ears like a bat's.

Re-shape the face. Make it bony with a pointed chin like this.

Use a light pencil for your original drawing so that you can rub it out easily later.

Make the head bulge and take away the hair. Add some scales.

A skinny neck and a strange skin colour make it really gruesome.

What do you think *you* would look
like if you lived on another planet?

TRY IT YOURSELF - turn yourself into an alien!

So that's you
as an alien, Neil.
Quite an improvement,
I think.

Embossed Lettering

Have you ever seen embossed lettering? It's lettering that has been specially printed to stick up from the page. It looks really professional – and is expensive to produce. But you can create your own. It looks great on invitations and even posters!

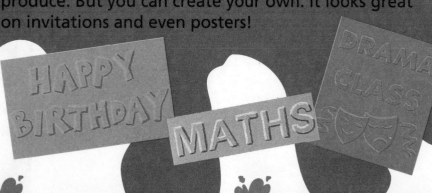

Take some coloured paper and two wax crayons. One should be lighter than the paper, the other darker.

First, draw thick chunky letters lightly in pencil.

Take your light crayon and pick out all the left-hand edges and the top edges of the lettering.

Take your dark crayon and draw along the right-hand edges and bottom edges of the lettering.

NOW TRY EMBOSSING THIS.

I HOPE YOU ENJOYED MY ART ATTACK BOOK. NEIL

Always use coloured paper! And look out for curved letters. Make sure you blend in the shading.

WAX CRAYON